MATHS

FOR PRACTICE & REVISION

2

FACTORS

PROPORTION

LINEAR MEASUREMENT

APPROXIMATIONS & STANDARD FORM

PERIMETER, AREA & VOLUME

PETER ROBSON

 **Newby Books**

PO BOX 40, SCARBOROUGH
NORTH YORKSHIRE, YO12 5TW
TEL/FAX 01723 362713
www.newbybooks.co.uk

FINDING ALL THE FACTORS OF A NUMBER

e.g. Find all the factors of 84.

*1) Divide by 1 $\frac{84}{1} = $ **84**

Factors are 1 and 84

*2) Divide by 2 if possible $\frac{84}{2} = $ **42**

Factors are 1,2,42,84

*3) Divide by 3 if possible $\frac{84}{3} = $ **28**

Factors are 1,2,3,28,42,84

*4) Divide by 4 if possible $\frac{84}{4} = $ **21**

Factors are 1,2,3,4,21,28,42,84

*5) Divide by 5 if possible   NOT POSSIBLE

*6) Divide by 6 if possible $\frac{84}{6} = $ **14**

Factors are 1,2,3,4,6,14,21,28,42,84

*7) Divide by 7 if possible $\frac{84}{7} = $ **12**

Factors are 1,2,3,4,6,7,12,14,21,28,42,84

No more numbers between 7 and 12 will divide into 84, so **the factors of 84 are**

1, 2, 3, 4, 6, 7, 12, 14, 21, 28, 42 and 84.

 # PRIME NUMBERS

A PRIME NUMBER is a number which has only TWO factors (<u>1</u> and <u>itself</u>), e.g. 47 is a prime number; its only factors are 1 and 47.

The PRIME NUMBERS up to 50 are

2, 3, 5, 7, 11, 13, 17, 19, 23, 29, 31, 37, 41, 43, 47.

FINDING THE PRODUCT OF PRIME NUMBERS

e.g. Find the value of $2 \times 3 \times 5$

*Multiply $2 \times 3 \times 5 \; = \; \underline{30}$

e.g. Find the value of $3 \times 3 \times 3 \times 7$

$3 \times 3 \times 3 \times 7 \; = \; \underline{189}$

a   Find all the factors of each of these numbers

1)	10	6)	28	11)	54	16)	44
2)	30	7)	16	12)	35	17)	64
3)	18	8)	56	13)	72	18)	90
4)	15	9)	66	14)	20	19)	25
5)	24	10)	100	15)	6	20)	52

---

b   Find all the factors of each of these numbers.
Write PRIME against your answer if the number is prime

1)	45	6)	9	11)	29	16)	11
2)	112	7)	31	12)	36	17)	8
3)	17	8)	150	13)	60	18)	67
4)	88	9)	51	14)	43	19)	144
5)	40	10)	27	15)	12	20)	65

---

c   Find the value of each of these groups of prime numbers

1)	2 x 2 x 2	6)	3 x 5 x 5	11)	2 x 7 x 11
2)	2 x 3	7)	2 x 5 x 7	12)	2 x 2 x 2 x 3
3)	2 x 3 x 3	8)	2 x 3 x 11	13)	2 x 29
4)	2 x 2 x 5	9)	3 x 3 x 5	14)	3 x 3 x 13
5)	2 x 2 x 2 x 2	10)	5 x 5 x 5	15)	3 x 3 x 3 x 3

---

d   Find the value of each of these groups

1)	2 x 11 x 11	6)	7 x 11 x 13	11)	3 x 3 x 3 x 7
2)	3 x 7	7)	2 x 2 x 2 x 2 x 2 x 2	12)	2 x 3 x 5 x 7
3)	2 x 2 x 3 x 3	8)	2 x 2 x 23	13)	11 x 13 x 13
4)	5 x 5 x 11	9)	2 x 3 x 17	14)	2 x 2 x 3 x 31
5)	3 x 3 x 5 x 5	10)	7 x 7 x 7	15)	2 x 2 x 2 x 5 x 5 x 5

PRIME FACTORS

e.g. Express 60 as a product of prime factors

*1) Divide by the lowest possible prime number

$$\begin{array}{c|c} 2 & 60 \\ \hline & 30 \end{array}$$

*2) Divide by the lowest possible prime number

$$\begin{array}{c|c} 2 & 60 \\ 2 & 30 \\ \hline & 15 \end{array}$$

*3) Divide by the lowest possible prime number

$$\begin{array}{c|c} 2 & 60 \\ 2 & 30 \\ 3 & 15 \\ \hline & 5 \end{array}$$

*4) Divide by the lowest possible prime number. Go on doing this until the answer is 1.

$$\begin{array}{c|c} 2 & 60 \\ 2 & 30 \\ 3 & 15 \\ 5 & 5 \\ \hline & 1 \end{array}$$

$$60 \;=\; 2 \times 2 \times 3 \times 5$$

e.g. (2) Express 72 as a product of prime factors

$$\begin{array}{c|c} 2 & 72 \\ 2 & 36 \\ 2 & 18 \\ 3 & 9 \\ 3 & 3 \\ \hline & 1 \end{array}$$

$72 = 2 \times 2 \times 2 \times 3 \times 3$

e.g. (3) Express 45 as a product of prime factors

$$\begin{array}{c|c} 3 & 45 \\ 3 & 15 \\ 5 & 5 \\ \hline & 1 \end{array}$$

$45 = 3 \times 3 \times 5$

WRITING PRIME FACTORS IN SHORT

The product of numbers can often be written in short,

e.g. $2 \times 2 \times 2 \times 2 \times 2$ can be written 2^5.

The ^{5} is called the power (or index) of 2

2^5 is '2 to the power 5'

e.g. 3×3 can be written 3^2

$5 \times 5 \times 5$ can be written 5^3

$2 \times 2 \times 3 \times 3 \times 5$ can be written $2^2 \times 3^2 \times 5$

$2 \times 3 \times 3 \times 3 \times 7 \times 11 \times 11$ can be written

$$2 \times 3^3 \times 7 \times 11^2$$

a Express each number as a product of prime factors

1)	18	5)	6	9)	66	13)	36	17)	27
2)	56	6)	50	10)	40	14)	28	18)	76
3)	12	7)	24	11)	75	15)	120	19)	168
4)	32	8)	15	12)	110	16)	88	20)	100

b Express each number as a product of prime factors

1)	200	5)	121	9)	105	13)	210	17)	78
2)	86	6)	68	10)	126	14)	65	18)	84
3)	188	7)	80	11)	16	15)	114	19)	187
4)	30	8)	93	12)	92	16)	770	20)	324

c Write each of these groups of prime numbers in short,

e.g. $2 \times 2 \times 2 \times 2 \times 3 \times 5 \times 5 \times 7 \times 7 \times 7 = 2^4 \times 3 \times 5^2 \times 7^3$

1) $2 \times 2 \times 2 \times 2 \times 2 \times 2$

2) $2 \times 2 \times 2 \times 3 \times 3 \times 5 \times 5$

3) $3 \times 3 \times 3 \times 7 \times 7 \times 7$

4) $2 \times 2 \times 2 \times 2 \times 11 \times 11$

5) $2 \times 2 \times 3 \times 3 \times 5 \times 5 \times 5$

6) $2 \times 2 \times 2 \times 7 \times 7 \times 13$

7) $3 \times 3 \times 3 \times 3 \times 3$

8) $5 \times 5 \times 17 \times 17 \times 17$

9) $2 \times 3 \times 3 \times 3 \times 7 \times 7$

10) $2 \times 2 \times 5 \times 5 \times 5 \times 5$

11) $11 \times 11 \times 11 \times 11$

12) $2 \times 2 \times 3 \times 3 \times 7 \times 7 \times 19 \times 19$

13) $2 \times 2 \times 2 \times 3 \times 3 \times 3 \times 3$

14) $23 \times 23 \times 23$

15) $3 \times 3 \times 7 \times 11 \times 11$

d Find the value of each of these groups

(e.g. $2^4 \times 3 \times 5 = 2 \times 2 \times 2 \times 2 \times 3 \times 5 = 240$)

1)	$2^3 \times 3^2$	5)	$2^2 \times 5^3$	8)	7×11^2
2)	3×5^2	6)	$3^4 \times 11$	9)	$2^4 \times 13$
3)	$2^2 \times 3^3$	7)	$2^2 \times 3^2 \times 5^2$	10)	$2^3 \times 11^3$
4)	$2 \times 3 \times 7^2$				

e Express each number as a product of prime factors.
Write your answer IN SHORT

1)	44	5)	48	9)	726	13)	144	17)	1125
2)	81	6)	216	10)	625	14)	90	18)	343
3)	392	7)	64	11)	396	15)	1323	19)	1936
4)	2000	8)	152	12)	225	16)	576	20)	729

H.C.F. (HIGHEST COMMON FACTOR)

The H.C.F. of a group of numbers is the highest factor which is common to all the numbers — in other words, the highest amount which will divide into all the numbers.

e.g. Find the H.C.F. of 180, 126, and 72

*1) Express each number as a product of prime factors

2	180		2	126		2	72
2	90		3	63		2	36
3	45		3	21		2	18
3	15		7	7		3	9
5	5			1		3	3
	1						1

*2) Find which factors are common to each group

②	180		②	126		②	72
2	90		③	63		2	36
③	45		③	21		2	18
③	15		7	7		③	9
5	5			1		③	3
	1						1

*3) Multiply   2 × 3 × 3   =   18

H.C.F. of 180, 126 and 72   is   18

---

e.g. (2) Find the H.C.F. of 105 and 30

105 = ③ × ⑤ × 7
30   = 2 × ③ × ⑤

H.C.F. of 105 and 30   is   3 × 5   =   15

If the groups have **no prime factors in common,** the H.C.F. is 1.

e.g.   Find the H.C.F. of 35 and 66

35 = 5 × 7
66 = 2 × 3 × 11

H.C.F. of 35 and 66   is   1.

a Find the H.C.F. of each group

1) 14, 16	6) 15, 35	11) 132, 60	16) 42, 6
2) 24, 15	7) 22, 32	12) 45, 33	17) 72, 36
3) 50, 20	8) 96, 40	13) 28, 42	18) 63, 35
4) 30, 18	9) 36, 63	14) 120, 100	19) 45, 18
5) 56, 36	10) 48, 80	15) 45, 75	20) 21, 27

---

b Find the H.C.F. of each group

1) 48, 60, 78	6) 90, 135	11) 154, 165
2) 105, 48	7) 8, 20, 6	12) 9, 24, 39
3) 28, 16, 40	8) 48, 72, 120	13) 36, 90
4) 55, 65, 20	9) 78, 130	14) 72, 12, 102
5) 54, 180	10) 84, 21	15) 102, 68

---

c Find the H.C.F. of each group

1) 156, 52	6) 336, 96, 144	11) 210, 504
2) 108, 18, 54	7) 60, 105	12) 48, 300
3) 80, 30, 100	8) 20, 16, 12	13) 66, 30, 54, 12
4) 88, 56	9) 180, 72	14) 270, 216
5) 154, 70	10) 99, 54	15) 325, 175

---

d Find the H.C.F. of each group. If a group has no prime factors in common, write 'H.C.F. is 1'

1) 66, 70	6) 315, 140	11) 7, 27, 37
2) 176, 110	7) 28, 55	12) 132, 330
3) 40, 27	8) 184, 256, 112	13) 210, 84, 56
4) 56, 175, 21	9) 18, 45, 10	14) 44, 63
5) 364, 1001	10) 156, 117	15) 102, 84, 114

L.C.M. (LOWEST COMMON MULTIPLE)

The L.C.M. of a group of numbers is the lowest multiple that **all** the numbers will divide into.

e.g. Find the L.C.M. of 20 and 18

```
2| 20          2| 18
2| 10          3|  9
5|  5          3|  3
 |  1           |  1
```

Largest group of 2's in any one column is   2 x 2
Largest group of 3's in any one column is   3 x 3
Largest group of 5's in any one column is   5

so L.C.M. of 20 and 18 is $2 \times 2 \times 3 \times 3 \times 5$ (or $2^2 \times 3^2 \times 5$)

$$= \quad 180$$

e.g. Find the L.C.M. of 6, 8, 28

```
2| 6        2| 8        2| 28
3| 3        2| 4        2| 14
 | 1        2| 2        7|  7
            |  1         |  1
```

Largest group of 2's in any one column is   2 x 2 x 2
Largest group of 3's in any one column is   3
Largest group of 7's in any one column is   7

so L.C.M. of 6, 8, 28 = $2 \times 2 \times 2 \times 3 \times 7$

(or $2^3 \times 3 \times 7$)   =   168

e.g. Find the L.C.M. of 50, 16, 18. Leave your answer as a product of prime factors.

```
2| 50        2| 16        2| 18
5| 25        2|  8        3|  9
5|  5        2|  4        3|  3
 |  1        2|  2         |  1
             |  1
```

so L.C.M. of 50, 16, 18 is $2 \times 2 \times 2 \times 2 \times 3 \times 3 \times 5 \times 5$

or $2^4 \times 3^2 \times 5^2$

ASCENDING ORDER

Always write prime factors in ASCENDING order (going up), starting with the smallest number first.

e.g. $2^2 \times 3^4 \times 5 \times 11^2$ (**not** $3^4 \times 11^2 \times 2^2 \times 5$, etc.)

$3^3 \times 5^2 \times 7^2$ (**not** $7^2 \times 3^3 \times 5^2$, etc.)

a Find the L.C.M. of each group

1)	12, 9	6)	14, 10	11)	12, 14	16)	8, 10, 12
2)	15, 24	7)	25, 15	12)	25, 30	17)	5, 11
3)	42, 30	8)	12, 16	13)	22, 18	18)	54, 12
4)	16, 8	9)	24, 6, 8	14)	35, 15	19)	9, 6
5)	27, 60	10)	44, 33	15)	10, 32	20)	15, 8

---

b Find the L.C.M. of each group

1)	48, 32	6)	9, 6, 8	11)	7, 11, 13	16)	25, 20
2)	3, 10, 4	7)	16, 20	12)	24, 36	17)	3, 4, 5, 6
3)	6, 76	8)	24, 28	13)	2, 3, 4	18)	42, 36
4)	18, 52	9)	8, 6, 10	14)	28, 14	19)	15, 20, 25
5)	12, 4, 6	10)	36, 99	15)	124, 155	20)	116, 174

---

c Find the L.C.M. of each group. Leave your answer as a product of prime factors in ascending order.

1)	56, 60	6)	130, 231	11)	98, 68
2)	14, 18, 22	7)	32, 34, 37	12)	32, 42, 52
3)	125, 27, 8	8)	150, 275	13)	21, 18, 15
4)	36, 242	9)	54, 48	14)	66, 76
5)	84, 81	10)	33, 77, 55	15)	243, 144

---

d Find the H.C.F. and L.C.M. of each group. Remember — if a group has no prime factors in common, the H.C.F. is 1.

1)	8, 6	6)	24, 16	11)	27, 25
2)	12, 20	7)	45, 105	12)	63, 18
3)	24, 54	8)	72, 36	13)	50, 125, 175
4)	5, 6, 8	9)	40, 50	14)	308, 84
5)	36, 48	10)	21, 24	15)	14, 15, 16

SQUARES

The SQUARE of a number is **the number multiplied by itself.**

e.g.   Find the square of 87

$$87 \times 87 \ = \ 7569$$

e.g. Find the square of $2\frac{1}{3}$

$$2\frac{1}{3} \times 2\frac{1}{3} \ = \ \frac{7}{3} \times \frac{7}{3} = \ \frac{49}{9} \ = \ 5\frac{4}{9}$$

SQUARED can be written **to the power 2**.

e.g.   Find the value of 23^2

$$23^2 \ = \ 23 \times 23 \ = \ 529$$

e.g.   Find the value of $(5\frac{1}{2})^2$

$$(5\frac{1}{2})^2 \ = \ 5\frac{1}{2} \times 5\frac{1}{2} \ = \ 30\frac{1}{4}$$

CUBES

The CUBE of a number is **the number multiplied by itself and then by itself again.**

e.g.   Find the cube of 12

$$12 \times 12 \times 12 \ = \ 1728$$

CUBED can be written **to the power 3**

e.g.   Find the value of 26^3

$$26^3 \ = \ 26 \times 26 \times 26 \ = \ 17576$$

e.g.   Find the value of $(\frac{1}{4})^3$

$$(\frac{1}{4})^3 \ = \ \frac{1}{4} \times \frac{1}{4} \times \frac{1}{4} \ = \ \frac{1}{64}$$

OTHER POWERS

'To the power 4' means 'times itself times itself times itself'

e.g. $5^4 \ = \ 5 \times 5 \times 5 \times 5 \ = \ 625$

Higher powers work just the same way

e.g. $4^5 \ = \ 4 \times 4 \times 4 \times 4 \times 4 \ = \ 1024$

$$(1\frac{1}{2})^6 \ = \ 1\frac{1}{2} \times 1\frac{1}{2} \times 1\frac{1}{2} \times 1\frac{1}{2} \times 1\frac{1}{2} \times 1\frac{1}{2}$$
$$= \ \frac{3}{2} \times \frac{3}{2} \times \frac{3}{2} \times \frac{3}{2} \times \frac{3}{2} \times \frac{3}{2} \ = \ \frac{729}{64} = 11\frac{25}{64}$$

a Find the square of each of these numbers

1) 8	6) 21	11) 12	16) 9
2) 13	7) 11	12) 105	17) 46
3) 6	8) 123	13) 77	18) 68
4) 15	9) 16	14) 18	19) 82
5) 48	10) 33	15) 29	20) 232

---

b Find the square of each of these

1) 2.7	4) 6.1	7) 14	10) $^3/_5$
2) 73	5) $^2/_3$	8) 1¾	
3) 1½	6) 4.7	9) 0.9	

---

c Find the value of each of these

1) $(1.25)^2$	5) $(0.8)^2$	9) $(^5/_8)^2$	13) 500^2
2) 44^2	6) 111^2	10) 26^2	14) $(^1/_6)^2$
3) $(2½)^2$	7) $(0.04)^2$	11) $(1¼)^2$	15) $(13.5)^2$
4) 30^2	8) 99^2	12) 54^2	

---

d Find the cube of each of these numbers

1) 4	4) 1.5	7) 200	10) 71
2) 17	5) 10	8) ½	
3) 1⅓	6) 0.6	9) 5	

---

e Find the value of each of these

1) 3^4	6) 2^4	11) $(4½)^2$	16) $(0.3)^3$
2) 62^2	7) 1^6	12) 3^5	17) 20^4
3) 2^5	8) $(^2/_3)^4$	13) 11^3	18) 2^7
4) 5^2	9) 19^2	14) $(3.2)^2$	19) 8^3
5) 7^3	10) 1000^3	15) 6^4	20) $(0.1)^4$

SQUARE ROOTS

The SQUARE ROOT is the number from which a square is formed

e.g.   The square of 7 $=$ 7×7 $=$ 49
so the SQUARE ROOT of 49 is 7

Square root can be written $\sqrt{}$ or $\sqrt{}$ so $\sqrt{49} = 7$

e.g.   Find the value of $\sqrt{3\frac{6}{25}}$

$$\sqrt{3\tfrac{6}{25}} = \sqrt{\tfrac{81}{25}} = \frac{\sqrt{81}}{\sqrt{25}} = \frac{9}{5} = 1\tfrac{4}{5}$$

SQUARE ROOTS FROM PRIME FACTORS
e.g.   Find the square root of 324

2	324
2	162
3	81
3	27
3	9
3	3
	1

*1)   Express as a product of prime factors

*2)   Split factors into two equal groups
$$324 \ = \ \underline{2 \times 3 \times 3} \ \times \ \underline{2 \times 3 \times 3}$$

*3)   The square root is ONE of the groups
$$= \ 2 \times 3 \times 3 \ = \ \mathbf{18}$$

e.g. (2) Find the square root of 1764

2	1764
2	882
3	441
3	147
7	49
7	7
	1

$1764 = 2 \times 3 \times 7$
$ \times 2 \times 3 \times 7$

$\sqrt{1764} = 2 \times 3 \times 7$
$\phantom{\sqrt{1764}} = \underline{\mathbf{42}}$

e.g. (3) Find the value of
$$\sqrt{24 \times 54}$$

2	24
2	12
2	6
3	3
	1

2	54
3	27
3	9
3	3
	1

$24 \times 54 =$
$\underline{2 \times 2 \times 3 \times 3}$
$\underline{\times 2 \times 2 \times 3 \times 3}$

$\sqrt{24 \times 54} =$
$\underline{2 \times 2 \times 3 \times 3 = \mathbf{36}}$

COMPLETING A PERFECT SQUARE

e.g.   What is the lowest number by which 392 must be multiplied to make a perfect square?
$$392 \ = \ 2 \times 2 \times 2 \times 7 \times 7$$
$$\text{or } \underline{2 \times 2 \times 7} \times \underline{2 \times \times 7}$$
$$\uparrow$$

392 must be multiplied by **2** to make a perfect square.

1 From your knowledge of 'times tables', write down the square root of each of these

1)	64	*3)*	100	*5)*	4	*7)*	1	*9)*	144
2)	9	*4)*	25	*6)*	121	*8)*	16	*10)*	36

---

2 Find the value of each of these

1) $\sqrt{\frac{1}{9}}$ *3)* $\sqrt{81}$ *5)* $\sqrt{\frac{9}{25}}$ *7)* $\sqrt{6\frac{1}{4}}$ *9)* $\sqrt{\frac{81}{121}}$

2) $\sqrt{\frac{16}{25}}$ *4)* $\sqrt{\frac{36}{49}}$ *6)* $\sqrt{2\frac{7}{9}}$ *8)* $\sqrt{\frac{49}{144}}$ *10)* $\sqrt{3\frac{1}{16}}$

---

3 Express each of these as a product of prime factors, and hence find the square root of each

1)	196	*4)*	900	*7)*	2304	*10)*	1089	*13)*	225
2)	576	*5)*	256	*8)*	484	*11)*	400	*14)*	2916
3)	1024	*6)*	2025	*9)*	625	*12)*	3136	*15)*	3969

---

4 By expressing as prime factors, find the values of

1) $\sqrt{784}$ *4)* $\sqrt{1296}$ *7)* $\sqrt{96 \times 54}$ *10)* $\sqrt{68 \times 153}$

2) $\sqrt{1936}$ *5)* $\sqrt{2500}$ *8)* $\sqrt{72 \times 32}$

3) $\sqrt{729}$ *6)* $\sqrt{6084}$ *9)* $\sqrt{56 \times 126}$

---

5 By expressing each of these as a product of prime factors, find the lowest number by which each must be multiplied to make a perfect square

1)	588	*4)*	80	*7)*	92	*10)*	684
2)	32	*5)*	63	*8)*	96		
3)	396	*6)*	160	*9)*	28		

QUANTITIES FROM UNITS

e.g.   Find the cost of 8 at 85p each.

*Multiply 8×85 =   680p   =   £6.80

e.g. (2) Find the total length of 17 boxes, each 24 centimetres long, placed end to end.

$$17 \times 24 = 408 \text{ centimetres}$$

Money

If the answer comes to £1 or more, it is better to give the answer in £

e.g. $16 \times 52p$ =   832p   =   £8.32

 # UNITS FROM QUANTITIES

e.g.   If 7 items cost £8.75, what is the cost of 1?

*Divide $8.75 \div 7$ (or $\frac{8.75}{7}$)   =   £1.25

e.g. (2)   What is the UNIT cost if 36 items cost £77.40?

$$\frac{77.40}{36} = £2.15$$

e.g. (3)   If 2500 tins of fruit cost £950, what is the cost of 1 tin of fruit?

$$\frac{950}{2500} = £0.38 \text{ or } 38p$$

a

Find the cost of

1)	6 at £2 each	6)	24 at £1.60 each	11)	11 at £1328 each
2)	5 at 75p each	7)	7 at £3.75 each	12)	8 at 93p each
3)	4 at £3.20 each	8)	15 at £84 each	13)	300 at £2.40 each
4)	13 at 4p each	9)	3 at £12.65 each	14)	2 ½ at £75.50 each
5)	9 at £2675 each	10)	72 at 42p each	15)	55 at 62p each

---

b

1) Find the cost of 12 bus tickets at 74p each.
2) What is the cost of 3 electronic games at £18.85 each?
3) If 1 box contains 73 matches, how many matches are there in 9 similar boxes?
4) What is the mass of 16 similar blocks of metal weighing 527 grams each?
5) Find the cost of 100 watches at £14.95 each.
6) Each row in a theatre will seat 33 people. How many people can be seated in 14 rows?
7) How much would 25 stamps cost at 25p each?
8) A jigsaw puzzle was made up of 235 pieces. How many pieces would there be altogether in 17 of the same sort of puzzle?
9) Find the cost of 64 newspapers at 28p each.
10) If a film contains 36 photographs, how many photographs can be taken with 8 films?

---

c

1) 9 cans of ginger beer cost £1.71. What is the cost of 1 can?
2) If 7 copies of a book cost £26.25, what does 1 copy cost?
3) In 24 similar packets there is a total of 360 toffees. How many toffees are there in each packet?
4) How much does 1 jar of pickle cost if 12 jars cost £9.96?
5) A party of 630 people can be seated exactly in 14 similar buses. How many seats has each bus?
6) Find the unit cost if 8 items cost £71.20.
7) A restaurant paid £270 for 1500 ice creams. What was the cost of 1 ice cream?
8) If 8 mugs will hold a total of 2.4 litres of lemonade, how much will 1 mug hold?
9) What is the cost of 1 tape cassette if 20 cost £24.60?
10) If a factory produced 24 tonnes of a chemical in 4 ½ hours, how many tonnes would it produce in 1 hour?

QUANTITIES FROM QUANTITIES

e.g.   If 8 oranges cost 72p, how much would 13 oranges cost?

$$8 \text{ oranges cost } 72p$$
$$1 \text{ orange costs } \tfrac{72}{8} \, p$$
$$13 \text{ oranges cost } \tfrac{72}{8} \times \tfrac{13}{1} = 117p = \underline{£1.17}$$

e.g.   If 6 pints of milk fill exactly 21 plastic cartons, how many cartons could be filled with 16 pints of milk?

$$6 \text{ pints fill } 21 \text{ cartons}$$
$$1 \text{ pint fills } \tfrac{21}{6} \text{ cartons}$$
$$16 \text{ pints fill } \tfrac{21}{6} \times \tfrac{16}{1} = \underline{56 \text{ cartons}}$$

 Always put WHAT YOU ARE TRYING TO FIND on the RIGHT

e.g.   A car goes 130 miles on 25 litres of petrol.
How much petrol would it need to go 247 miles?

Put   LITRES   on the right

$$\text{Car goes } 130 \text{ miles on } 25 \text{ litres}$$
$$1 \text{ mile on } \tfrac{25}{130} \text{ litres}$$
$$247 \text{ miles on } \tfrac{25}{130} \times \tfrac{247}{1}$$
$$= \underline{47.5 \text{ litres}}$$

e.g.   A car goes 130 miles on 25 litres of petrol.
How far would it go on 55 litres of petrol?

Put MILES on the right

$$\text{Car uses } 25 \text{ litres to go } 130 \text{ miles}$$
$$1 \text{ litre to go } \tfrac{130}{25} \text{ miles}$$
$$55 \text{ litres to go } \tfrac{130}{25} \times \tfrac{55}{1}$$
$$= \underline{286 \text{ miles}}$$

1) What is the cost of 15 footballs if 9 footballs cost £71.55?
2) 6 tins of carrots cost £1.62. How much do 22 tins cost?
3) How much would 4 pairs of jeans cost if 7 pairs cost £76.65?
4) If 3 ice creams cost 69p, what is the cost of 13 ice creams?
5) Ten buckets will hold 145 litres of water. How much water will 19 buckets hold?
6) What is the price of 12 tractors if 5 cost £63750?
7) In eight packets there are 112 biscuits. How many biscuits are there in 20 packets?
8) If 4 copies of a magazine cost £1.80, find the cost of 14 copies.
9) How many coloured pencils would there be in 11 tins if 25 tins contained 300 pencils?
10) What would 7 tubes of toothpaste cost if 15 tubes cost £9.45?

REMEMBER to put **WHAT YOU ARE TRYING TO FIND** on the **RIGHT**

1) If 5 trucks can transport 45 tonnes of sand, how many trucks will be needed to transport 108 tonnes?
2) Twelve kettles could be bought at an ironmonger's for £42. How many kettles could be bought for £77?
3) One day the ticket man at a toll bridge collected £225 when 300 cars passed over the bridge. How much money should the man have collected the next day if 186 cars passed over the bridge?
4) If 56 pupils can be carried in 4 minibuses, how many minibuses will be needed to carry 126 pupils?
5) Four fruit buns cost 38p. What would be the cost of 72 buns?
6) 315 litres of diesel oil a day are needed to keep 3 generators going. How much oil would be needed to fuel 8 generators of the same kind?
7) Seven similar parcels weigh 19.6 kg altogether. How much would 22 of these parcels weigh altogether?
8) 75 litres of paraffin will just fill 6 cans. How much paraffin will be needed to fill 44 cans?
9) 5 electronic calculators can be bought for £90. What number of calculators could I buy for £500 and what would be the exact cost of this number?
10) A family uses 18 tea bags each day. How many boxes, each containing 160 bags, must they buy to be sure of having enough bags for 4 weeks?

RATIO

Ratio is a way of comparing the sizes of two or more quantities.

Ratio is usually written with COLONS

e.g. $3 : 7 : 9$

e.g. Toby is 5 years old and Gary is 12 years old.
What is the ratio of Toby's age to Gary's?

$5 : 12$

Ratios are written as WHOLE NUMBERS without units.

 # LOWEST TERMS

Ratios should always be written in their lowest terms.
Divide by the Highest Common Factor of all the numbers (see page 6)

e.g. Write the ratio $4 : 10 : 12$ in its lowest terms

$4 : 10 : 12$ will all divide by 2, so the correct ratio is
$2 : 5 : 6$

e.g. Peter has 36 marbles and John has 42 marbles.
Express these quantities as a ratio in its lowest terms.

$36 : 42$ will both divide by 6, so the correct ratio is $6 : 7$.

 # DECIMALS AND FRACTIONS

Ratios should always be expressed as WHOLE NUMBERS.

If ratio contains **decimals,** multiply all through by 10, 100, 1000, etc. to make all quantities into whole numbers.

e.g. $1.83 : 2.5 \times 100 = 183 : 250$

e.g. $2.8 : 3.5 : 5.6 \times 10 = 28 : 35 : 56$ which then divides by 7 to give $4 : 5 : 8$

If ratio contains **fractions,** multiply all through by the lowest common denominator

e.g. $1\frac{1}{4} : 2\frac{1}{4} \times 4 = 5 : 9$

e.g. $2\frac{2}{3} : 5\frac{1}{2} \times 6 = 16 : 33$

A Write the ratios correctly in their lowest terms

1)	4 : 2	6)	21 : 9	11)	28 : 35
2)	25 : 35	7)	400 : 100	12)	16 : 32 : 40
3)	18 : 12	8)	5 : 10: 30	13)	33 : 24
4)	2 : 6	9)	75 : 45	14)	12 : 4 : 8
5)	4 : 12 : 24	10)	18 : 12 : 4	15)	36 : 30

B Express these ratios correctly as whole numbers in their lowest terms

1)	1.2 : 2.3	6)	$1\frac{1}{5} : 2\frac{2}{5} : 1\frac{1}{5}$	11)	$7\frac{1}{2} : 6\frac{1}{4}$
2)	$5\frac{1}{2} : 4\frac{1}{2}$	7)	14.4 : 9.6	12)	0.25 : 1.75 : 2.00
3)	$1\frac{2}{3} : 2\frac{2}{3}$	8)	$1\frac{1}{3} : 2\frac{1}{2}$	13)	$\frac{1}{6} : 2\frac{2}{3}$
4)	0.3 : 0.4 : 0.5	9)	3.2 : 4.8 : 8.0	14)	$\frac{4}{9} : \frac{1}{2} : \frac{2}{3}$
5)	2.8 : 1.6	10)	$\frac{1}{3} : \frac{1}{4}$	15)	0.15 : 0.075

C REMEMBER. All these answers should be given as WHOLE NUMBERS, without units, in their LOWEST TERMS.

1) In Class 3B there are 12 girls and 10 boys. What is the ratio of girls to boys?

2) There were 8 footballs, 12 hockey balls and 20 tennis balls in a sports cupboard. Express these amounts as a ratio.

3) A large can of shandy contains 440 ml and a small can contains 330 ml. Write these amounts as a ratio.

4) Of the 32 restaurants in a certain town, 4 are Chinese. What is the ratio of Chinese to **non-Chinese** restaurants in the town?

5) Two second-hand cars cost £2625 and £1875. Express these prices as a ratio.

6) Martin's height is 1.50 m and Paul's height is 1.38 m. What is the ratio of Martin's height to Paul's height?

7) A flower bed contained 104 tulips, of which 32 were yellow and the rest were red. What was the ratio of yellow tulips to **red tulips?**

8) During a football season, Alan scored 12 goals, Ben scored 18 goals and Chris scored 9 goals. Write the number of goals scored by Alan, Ben and Chris as a ratio.

9) Express £63, £56 and £42 as a ratio.

10) There are 6080 feet in a sea mile and 5280 feet in a land mile. Write these amounts as a ratio.

RATIO (2)

e.g. Harry and Tom receive pocket money in the ratio 4 : 3. If Harry receives 80p, how much does Tom receive?

In the ratio 4 : 3, Harry has 4 SHARES

$$4 \text{ SHARES} = 80p$$
$$1 \text{ SHARE} = {}^{80}\!/_{4} = 20p$$

Tom receives 3 SHARES = 20p × 3 = __60p__

A short way of writing this problem

(Stage 1)	Harry		Tom
Number of shares	4	:	3
	× 20p		
Real amounts	80p		

(Stage 2)	Harry		Tom
Number of shares	4	:	3
	× 20p		× 20p
Real amounts	80p		60p

---

e.g. (2) Robert's age, Aunt Sally's age and Uncle Nick's age are in the ratio 2 : 6 : 7. Uncle Nick is 42 years old. How old are Robert and Aunt Sally?

In the ratio 2 : 6 : 7, Uncle Nick has 7 shares

$$7 \text{ SHARES} = 42 \text{ years old}$$
$$1 \text{ SHARE} = {}^{42}\!/_{7} = 6 \text{ years old}$$

Robert is 2 SHARES = 6 × 2 = __12 years old__
Aunt Sally is 6 SHARES = 6 × 6 = __36 years old__

Robert	Aunt Sally	Uncle Nick
2	6	7
		× 6 years
		42 years etc.

1) Simon saved £45. The ratio of Simon's savings to his brother Edward's was 9 : 4. How much did Edward save?

2) The lengths of the rivers Paraná and Paraguay (in South America) are in the ratio 5 : 3. The Paraná is 2500 miles long. How long is the Paraguay?

3) The ratio of the heights of Amanda, Jane and Susan is 5 : 6 : 7. If Jane is 1.44 m tall, how tall is Amanda and how tall is Susan?

4) The populations of three towns are in the ratio 1 : 3 : 4. If the town with the **most** people has a population of 36000, what are the populations of the other two towns?

5) Peter scored 18 runs in a cricket match. The ratio of Peter's score to Mark's score was 2 : 7. What was Mark's score?

6) The ratio of the capacities (amounts they will hold) of a jug and a bucket is 2 : 5. If the bucket will hold 8¾ litres, how much will the jug hold?

7) An estate agent had three houses for sale. The prices of the houses were in the ratio 6 : 4 : 3 and the **cheapest** house was priced at £26250. What were the prices of the other two houses?

8) Three 'skyscraper' buildings have heights in the ratio 11 : 12 : 13. The tallest building is 247 m high. What heights are the other two buildings?

9) The number of players in the orchestras at Hillside School and St. Michael's School were in the ratio 7 : 10. If there were 28 players in Hillside School orchestra, how many were there in St. Michael's School orchestra?

10) The prices of two different kinds of tee-shirt were in the ratio 13 : 18. If the more expensive one cost £4.50, what did the cheaper one cost?

11) At King James' School the pupil : teacher ratio is 14 : 1. There are 17 teachers. How many pupils are there?

12) The number of horses racing on a certain day at Newmarket was in the ratio 17 : 7 to the number racing at Goodwood. If 42 horses raced at Goodwood, how many raced at Newmarket?

13) On a patch of ground the ratio of daisies to clovers was 16 : 3. If there were 27 clovers, how many daisies were there?

14) From London, the distances by air to Athens and Baghdad are in the ratio 10 : 17. Baghdad is 2550 miles from London. What distance from London is Athens?

15) Two railway locomotives had masses in the ratio 13 : 6. The lighter locomotive weighed 48 tonnes. How much did the heavier one weigh?

RATIO (3)

e.g.   Divide £627 between Andrew, Brenda and Charles in the ratio 2 : 4 : 5.

Andrew has   2 SHARES ⎫   Total number of shares
Brenda has   4 SHARES ⎬   2 + 4 + 5
Charles has   5 SHARES ⎭   = 11 SHARES

so EACH SHARE is $\frac{£627}{11}$ = £57

Andrew has   2 × £57 = £114
Brenda has   4 × £57 = £228
Charles has   5 × £57 = £285

(To check answer, £114 + £228 + £285 = £627)

A short way of writing this problem

(Stage 1)	Andrew		Brenda		Charles	TOTAL
Number of shares	2	:	4	:	5	11
						× **£57**
Real amounts						£627

(Stage 2)	Andrew	Brenda	Charles	TOTAL
Number of shares	2	4	5	11
	× **£57**	× **£57**	× **£57**	× **£57**
Real amounts	£114	£228	£285	£627

---

e.g. (2) Share 91 sweets between two boys in the ratio 4 : 3.

Total number of shares = 4 + 3 = 7

Each share is $\frac{91}{7}$ = 13 sweets

First boy   has   4 × 13 = 52 sweets
Second boy has   3 × 13 = 39 sweets

1st boy		2nd boy	TOTAL
4	:	3	7
			× **13 sweets**
			91 sweets etc.

1) Divide 96p in the ratio 1 : 5.
2) Divide 1430 miles in the ratio 3 : 3 : 4.
3) Share 585 eggs in the ratio 4 : 5.
4) Share £780 in the ratio 7 : 8.
5) Divide 602 beefburgers in the ratio 2 : 5 : 7.
6) Share £95 between Steven and Ray in the ratio 3 : 2.
7) Share 4½ tonnes of coal between Mr Allen and Mr Benson in the ratio 5 : 4.
8) 68 dog biscuits were shared between Rover and Butch in the ratio 1 : 1. How many did each dog get?
9) A prize of £1000 was shared between three people in the ratio 5 : 2 : 1. How much money did each person receive?
10) Share 75 chocolates between Emma and Lucy in the ratio 11 : 4.

---

1) A piece of timber 2.96 m long was cut into 3 pieces with lengths in the ratio 2 : 3 : 3. What lengths were the 3 pieces?
2) Three boys, Gary, Barry and Harry earned money by doing jobs in the holidays. Their earnings, which were in the ratio 8 : 6 : 3, came to a total of £59.50. Calculate how much each boy earned.
3) The ratio of people over 14 years of age to people under 14 years of age in a cinema audience was 8 : 3. If there were 253 people in the audience altogether, how many were under 14 years of age?
4) Anne and Frances picked 280 gooseberries. They decided to share the gooseberries in the ratio 9 : 11. Frances had the larger amount. How many gooseberries did Anne have?
5) Mrs Hubbard bought a television, a fridge and a vacuum cleaner. The prices were in the ratio 93 : 46 : 13 and Mrs Hubbard spent £478.80 altogether. What were the prices of the three things she bought?
6) The three sides of a triangle are in the ratio 3 : 4 : 5. If the total length of all the sides is 40.8 cm, what is the length of the longest side?
7) Two gardeners shared a plot of land in the ratio 9 : 7. The size of the plot was 920 square metres. How much land did each gardener get?
8) Robin, Stewart and William share a birthday cake in the ratio 5 : 4 : 3. Find how much of the cake each person receives, giving your answers as fractions in their lowest terms.
9) Sarah worked out that over a whole year, for every 2 hours spent at school, 13 hours were spent **not** at school. If there are 8760 hours in a year, how many hours in a year does she spend at school?
10) Brian walked from his house to the bus stop. Then he travelled by bus to school. The times he took to walk and go by bus were in the ratio 1 : 6. The whole journey took 42 minutes. How long did it take him to walk to the bus stop?

A LINEAR MEASUREMENT

METRES (m)   A **metre** is roughly as long as five
copies of this book
arranged like

A metre rule is usually printed with small divisions numbered
from 1 to 99 which are centimetres (hundredths of a metre).

To measure in metres, count the number of whole metres
and the number of divisions.

e.g.   If the thing you are measuring is 8 whole metres and
63 divisions, the length is 8.63 m.

e.g.   A distance of 4 metres and 7 divisions would be
written 4.07 m.

B CENTIMETRES (cm)   100cm = 1m

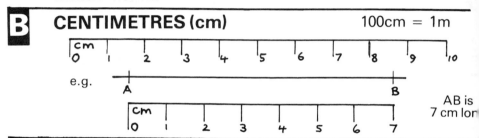

AB is
7 cm long

C CENTIMETRES AND TENTHS OF CENTIMETRES

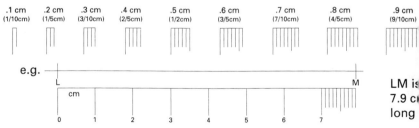

LM is
7.9 cm
long

D MILLIMETRES (mm)   1000mm = 1m

EF is 65
mm long

With a metre rule or trundle wheel, measure these.
Remember that the measurements should be written in
METRES, e.g. 19.35 m (not 19 m 35 cm).

1) Length of your classroom or bedroom.
2) Width of a football pitch, hockey pitch or tennis court.
3) Height of one of your friends or one of your family.
4) Length of school drive or front drive or path at home (Mind traffic!).
5) Width of a large room, like a gym or assembly hall.

Measure these lengths in CENTIMETRES

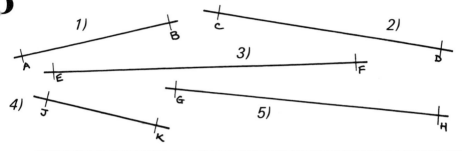

Measure these lengths in CENTIMETRES and TENTHS of CENTIMETRES

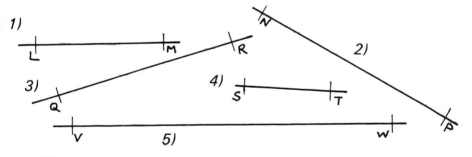

Measure these lengths in MILLIMETRES

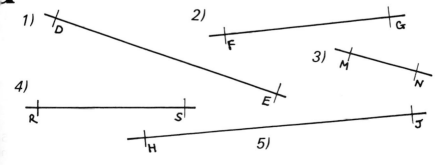

LINEAR MEASUREMENT (2)

Metric columns

kilo - (× 1000)	hecto - (× 100)	deca - (× 10)	* (1)	deci - (÷ 10)	centi - (÷ 100)	milli - (÷ 1000)

Length

kilo- metre km	(hecto- metre hm)	(deca- metre dam)	METRE m	(deci- metre dm)	centi- metre cm	milli- metre mm

(but hm, dam and dm are not often used)

Look at this number

2	5	6	1	7	8	3

*To express in METRES, put point after METRES column

2	5	6	1 ●	7	8	3 m

*To express in KILOMETRES, put point after KILOMETRES column

2 ●	5	6	1	7	8	3 km

*To express in CENTIMETRES, put point after CENTIMETRES column

2	5	6	1	7	8 ●	3 cm

e.g. Write in the correct columns

	km	—	—	m	—	cm	mm
5.38 m				5 ●	3	8	
4.25 km	4 ●	2	5				
79 cm					7	9 ●	

EXPRESSING IN OTHER UNITS

e.g. Express	km			m		cm	mm	
2.58 km in m	2 ●	5	8					
	2	5	8	0 ●				= 2580 m
54900 cm in km		5	9	4	0	0 ●		
	0 ●	5	9	4				= 0.594 km
23.127 m in cm				2	3 ●	1	2	7
				2	3	1	2 ●	7 = 2312.7 cm
35 km in cm	3	5 ●						
	3	5	0	0	0	0	0 ●	= 3500000 cm
6 mm in m							6	
				0 ●	0	0	6	= 0.006 m

FILL UP TO THE POINT WITH NOUGHTS IF NEEDED

I Express each of these numbers in (A) metres, (B) kilometres, (C) centimetres and (D) millimetres. Fill up to the point with noughts if needed.

e.g.

km	_	_	m	_	cm	mm
1	3	5	2	0	7	8

(A) 1352.078m,   (B) 1.352078km,   (C) 135207.8cm,
(D) 1352078 mm.

	km	_	_	m	_	cm	mm
1)	1	3	4	1	2	3	6
2)		6	5	3			
3)	9	2	7	8	1	2	
4)				6	8	1	4
5)				2	2		

	km	_	_	m	_	cm	mm	
6)	3							
7)	2	1	6	1	5	1	9	
8)		5	0	0		0		
9)						7	7	2
10)	8	5	4					

II Draw columns marked km, — , — , m, — , cm, mm and write these numbers in the correct columns

1) 91.2m	6) 599.9m	11) 0.3cm	16) 0.0264m
2) 4.569km	7) 88.1mm	12) 5566m	17) 17mm
3) 35000mm	8) 1.005m	13) 0.001km	18) 28.3km
4) 54.8cm	9) 360cm	14) 27.83cm	19) 5000m
5) 0.07m	10) 14.5km	15) 9095cm	20) 86.98m

III Express

1) 325 mm in cm	11) 2.45 cm in mm
2) 7 m in mm	12) 9 km in mm
3) 0.0865 km in cm	13) 0.0089 km in m
4) 24 cm in m	14) 1510 cm in mm
5) 3.7 km in m	15) 97.97 m in cm
6) 98000 mm in km	16) 125 cm in km
7) 333 mm in m	17) 840000 mm in m
8) 74000 cm in m	18) 3 mm in km
9) 0.161 m in mm	19) 683 m in cm
10) 3000 m in km	20) 77 m in km

LINEAR MEASUREMENT (3)

EXPRESSING IN OTHER UNITS (Quicker Way)

When expressing SMALL units as LARGER units, always DIVIDE (see table below)

    e.g. Express 538 mm in m

$$\frac{538}{1000} = 0.538 \text{ m}$$

When expressing LARGE units as SMALLER units, always MULTIPLY (see table below)

    e.g. Express 9.1 m in cm

$$9.1 \times 100 = 910 \text{ cm}$$

CONVERSION TABLE

m ⟶ km	÷	1000	mm ⟶ m	÷	1000
km ⟶ m	×	1000	m ⟶ mm	×	1000
cm ⟶ m	÷	100	mm ⟶ cm	÷	10
m ⟶ cm	×	100	cm ⟶ mm	×	10

SQUARE UNITS

To express SQUARE units as other SQUARE units, multiply or divide TWICE (see table above).

e.g. Express 82 km² (82 square kilometres) in square metres

*Multiply by 1000 and then by 1000 again

$$82 \times 1000 \times 1000 = 82000000 \text{ m}^2$$

e.g. Express 38 mm² in square centimetres

*Divide by 10 and then by 10 again

$$38 \div 10 \div 10 = 0.38 \text{ cm}^2$$

CUBIC UNITS

To express CUBIC units as other CUBIC units, multiply or divide THREE TIMES (see table above).

e.g. Express 90000 cm³ (90000 cubic centimetres) in cubic metres.

*Divide by 100, then by 100, then by 100

$$90000 \div 100 \div 100 \div 100 = 0.09 \text{ m}^3$$

1 Express

1)	2.95 km in m	5)	9035 mm in cm	8)	70000 m in km
2)	0.485 m in cm	6)	43 km in m	9)	6.12 m in cm
3)	6921 m in km	7)	0.85 m in mm	10)	6650 mm in m
4)	24.7 cm in mm				

2

1) Add 435.2 cm, 850.5 cm and 738 cm and express your answer in m
2) Express in m the sum of 0.75 km and 0.035 km
3) Find the value, in km, of 831 m x 47
4) Write in mm the value of 3.28 m + 6.77 m − 9.86m
5) Find the value of 2.25 m ÷ 9, giving your answer in cm
6) A running track was 200 m all the way round. Fiona ran 7 ½ times round the track. How far, in km, did she run?
7) A fence 3 km long starts at a concrete pillar and then has 250 wooden fence posts spaced along it at regular intervals, the last post being at the end of the fence. What is the distance, in metres between one fence post and the next?
8) 650 lengths of steel pipe are fitted end to end. Each length measures 25 m. Find the length, in km, of the complete pipe
9) A length of string 6.8 m long was cut into 8 equal shorter pieces. What was the length of each short piece in centimetres?
10) Each straight rail on Robert's model railway is 30 cm long. If he fixes 18 of these rails end to end, what length of railway, in metres, will he have?

3 Express

1) 6 square centimetres (6 cm²) in square millimetres (mm²)
2) 450 000 square metres (450 000 m²) in square kilometres (km²)

3)	2.5 km² in m²	7)	86 mm² in cm²
4)	72000 mm² in cm²	8)	3550 mm² in m²
5)	0.04 m² in cm²	9)	0.14 km² in m²
6)	9 m² in mm²	10)	9720 cm² in m²

4 Express

1) 8.25 cubic centimetres (8.25 cm³) in cubic millimetres (mm³)
2) 400000 cubic centimetres (400000 cm³) in cubic metres (m³)
3) 2 cubic metres (2 m³) in cubic millimetres (mm³)
4) 5150 cubic millimetres (mm³) in cubic centimetres (cm³)
5) 0.0000395 cubic metres (m³) in cubic centimetres (cm³)

APPROXIMATION 'TO THE NEAREST'

Sometimes, only a rough or **approximate** answer is needed.

e.g. The exact number of people living in a certain town in 21432.

What is 21432 correct to the nearest TEN? (rough answer)

*Stop at the TENS column   21430.

What is 21432 correct to the nearest HUNDRED?

(rougher answer still)

*Stop at the HUNDREDS column   21400.

What is 21432 correct to the nearest THOUSAND?

(even rougher answer)

*Stop at the THOUSANDS column   21000

What is 21432 correct to the nearest TEN THOUSAND?

(roughest possible answer)

*Stop at the TEN THOUSANDS column   20000

REMEMBER always to fill up to the point with noughts.

**VERY IMPORTANT — 'Five or more'

Always look at the NEXT digit after the one at which you are stopping. If it is 5 or more, your stopping number goes UP BY ONE.

e.g. 6859

To the nearest ten   6859 is 6860 (not 6850)

To the nearest hundred   6859 is 6900 (not 6800)

To the nearest thousand   6859 is 7000 (not 6000)

---

e.g. (2)   Express 16381 to the nearest hundred

16381   so the answer is 16400

---

e.g. (3)   Express 52.72 to the nearest whole number

52.72   so the answer is 53

a Write to the nearest TEN

1) 24	3) 83	5) 3465	7) 1111	9) 32917
2) 341	4) 168	6) 49	8) 876	10) 792

b Write to the nearest THOUSAND

1) 5230	3) 8721	5) 7379	7) 623500	9) 76966
2) 16446	4) 24198	6) 9850	8) 12095	10) 4775

c Write to the nearest HUNDRED

1) 5305	3) 777	5) 532	7) 55019	9) 92220
2) 46229	4) 34092	6) 6998	8) 4983	10) 4472

d Write to the nearest WHOLE NUMBER

1) 5.2	3) 3.62	5) 7.5	7) 178.1	9) 10.84
2) 16.7	4) 98.3	6) 39.9	8) 5.565	10) 108.4

e

1) A book has 684 pages. Write this number to the nearest hundred.
2) Multiply 68 by 57 and give your answer to the nearest ten.
3) The number of people who bought tickets for a pop concert was 8437. Express this number to the nearest thousand.
4) Find the sum of 5678, 2519 and 7393. Give your answer as an approximation to the nearest hundred.
5) Write the product of 309.7 and 0.4 to the nearest whole number.
6) Express 9766 kilometres to the nearest hundred kilometres.
7) Divide 5187 by 13 and express your answer to the nearest 10.
8) A flock of starlings contained 865 birds. Roughly how many birds were there in the flock, to the nearest hundred?
9) An author wrote a story containing 3888 words. How many words is this, correct to the nearest hundred?
10) Find the value of $100 \div 7$, expressed to the nearest whole number.

SIGNIFICANT FIGURES

Usually, the digits in a number, <u>not counting noughts at the beginning</u>, are SIGNIFICANT FIGURES (SIG.FIGS.)

e.g. <u>568</u> has 3 significant figures
<u>39572</u> has 5 significant figures
0.00<u>81</u> has 2 significant figures
<u>14.50</u> has 4 significant figures
0.<u>900</u> has 3 significant figures

Noughts at the end of a whole number are sometimes significant, sometimes not

e.g. 94000 may have 2, 3, 4 or 5 sig. figs.

 # CORRECTING TO SIGNIFICANT FIGURES

e.g. Write 2.543 correct to 2 sig.figs.

<u>2.5</u> (2 sig.figs.)

e.g. Correct 0.039815 to 3 sig.figs.

0.0<u>398</u> (3 sig.figs.)

Remember to fill up to the point with noughts if necessary.

e.g. Express £7290 correct to 1 sig.fig.

£<u>7</u>000 (1 sig.fig.)

**VERY IMPORTANT — 'Five or more'

Always look carefully at the <u>NEXT</u> digit after the one to which you are correcting. If this is <u>5 or more</u>, the <u>LAST DIGIT OF YOUR ANSWER GOES UP BY ONE</u>.

e.g. Write <u>36.3</u>58 to 3 sig.figs.
<u>36.4</u> (3 sig.figs)

e.g. Express <u>19</u>76 metres to 2 sig.figs.
<u>20</u>00 metres (2 sig.figs)

e.g. Write 0.009243797 correct to 4 sig.figs.
0.009<u>244</u>

How many significant figures has each of these numbers?

1)	625	3)	17328	5)	8	7)	0.01800	9)	0.0004
2)	0.44	4)	0.330	6)	4.775	8)	90	10)	500

Write these numbers correct to 2 significant figures.

1)	5.43	5)	0.0611	9)	0.456	13)	49670
2)	1722	6)	1.865	10)	293	14)	0.0823
3)	0.9815	7)	65387	11)	7684	15)	93.9
4)	474	8)	688	12)	1.175		

Write these numbers correct to 1 significant figure.

1)	2324	5)	27	9)	640000	13)	557
2)	71	6)	0.0925	10)	32.28	14)	0.0029
3)	646	7)	2983	11)	0.185	15)	9915
4)	0.052	8)	7.65	12)	477		

Calculate these

1) 12 x 16 correct to 1 sig. fig.
2) 2.45 x 7 correct to 3 sig. figs.
3) 500 ÷ 12 correct to 2 sig. figs.
4) 6973 + 5588 correct to 3 sig. figs.
5) 0.264 ÷ 0.6 correct to 1 sig. fig.
6) 1124 − 666 correct to 2 sig. figs.
7) 9.42 x 6.3 correct to 4 sig figs.
8) 56.3 + 48.7 + 9.2 correct to 2 sig. figs.
9) 0.067 x 0.37 correct to 3 sig. figs.
10) 26^2 correct to 1 sig. fig.

Express correct to 1 sig. fig.

1) the number of days in a year
2) the number of letters in the alphabet
3) the number of minutes in a week
4) the number of players in a cricket, hockey or soccer team
5) the number of hours from midday on Friday to midday on Saturday
6) the number of pages in this book (not counting the covers)
7) the number of weeks in a year
8) the sum of all the whole numbers from 1 to 12 inclusive
9) the telephone number (last five figures only) of the printer of this book, as shown inside the front cover
10) this year's date

ESTIMATION TO ONE SIG.FIG.

An estimation to 1 sig.fig. is the roughest possible answer to a problem.

e.g.   Estimate to 1 sig.fig. the value of

$$\frac{5.94 \times 6.38}{72.7}$$

*1)   Reduce all numbers to 2 sig.fig.

$$\frac{5.9 \times 6.4}{73}$$

*2)   Work out each part to 2 sig.figs.

$$\frac{37.76}{73} = \frac{38}{73}$$

*3)   Work out answer to 2 sig.figs.

$$0.52$$

*4)   Give answer to 1 sig.fig.

$$\frac{5.94 \times 6.38}{72.7} = 0.5 \text{ (1 sig.fig.)}$$

---

e.g. (2)   Find the value of $\dfrac{749 \times 823}{86 \times 219}$ to 1 sig.fig.

$$\frac{750 \times 820}{90 \times 220}$$

$$\frac{615000}{19800}$$

$$\frac{620000}{20000}$$

$$= 31$$

$$\frac{749 \times 823}{86 \times 219} = 30 \text{ (1 sig.fig.)}$$

Estimate each of these to 1 significant figure

1) 199 × 299
2) 62.3 × 60
3) 49.7 × 4.04
4) 31.6 ÷ 8
5) 0.923 × 0.321
6) 727 + 846 + 970 + 649
7) 987 − 293
8) 2.67 ÷ 30.3
9) 74729 + 88217
10) 16.875 × 3.025

Estimate each of these to 1 significant figure

1) 48.3 × 66
2) 8.95 × 1.125 × 7.5
3) 5371 ÷ 896
4) 68.375 × 7.27
5) 75.9 ÷ 187.1
6) 8773 + 7249 + 627
7) (6.985)²
8) 3.44 × 0.303
9) 6.924 ÷ 99
10) 3.125 × 36.47 × 8.11

Estimate each of these to 1 sig. fig.

1) $\dfrac{797 \times 496}{1334}$

2) $\dfrac{5.36 \times 10.75}{72.9}$

3) $\dfrac{272}{0.8 \times 5.6}$

4) $\dfrac{7.59 \div 3.245}{0.598}$

5) $\dfrac{3036 \times 414}{496 \times 357}$

6) $\dfrac{188.4 \div 5.615}{677}$

7) $\dfrac{948 \times 403}{128 \times 29}$

8) $\dfrac{32.7 \div 11.4}{1.76 \div 0.2}$

9) $\dfrac{6666 \times 2222}{7777}$

10) $\dfrac{0.28}{2.37 \div 59.9}$

DECIMAL PLACES

The digits after the point are DECIMAL PLACES

e.g. 11.<u>73</u> has 2 decimal places
6.<u>8875</u> has 4 decimal places
0.<u>092</u> has 3 decimal places
33.<u>4</u> has 1 decimal place

 # CORRECTING TO DECIMAL PLACES

e.g. Write 6.728 correct to 1 decimal place
6.<u>7</u>

Write 44.444 correct to 2 decimal places
44.<u>44</u>

Correct 0.000536 to 4 decimal places
0.<u>0005</u>

**VERY IMPORTANT — 'Five or more'

Always look carefully at the <u>NEXT</u> digit after the one to which you are correcting. If this is <u>5 or more</u>, the <u>LAST DIGIT OF YOUR ANSWER GOES UP BY ONE</u>.

e.g. Correct 0.<u>0865</u> to 2 decimal places
0.<u>09</u>↑

Write 15.<u>37</u> to 1 place of decimals
15.<u>4</u>↑

Write 0.<u>33961</u> to 3 places of decimals
0.<u>340</u>↑

a How many decimal places has each of these numbers?

1)	62.5	4)	20.05	7)	33.004	10)	0.00002
2)	1.874	5)	4.1667	8)	565.8		
3)	0.0927	6)	17.93	9)	724		

b Write these numbers correct to 1 decimal place

1)	8.94	5)	514.72	9)	0.307	13)	26.77
2)	76.36	6)	0.43	10)	15.97	14)	9.6550
3)	0.123	7)	62.89	11)	0.81	15)	0.944
4)	4.085	8)	9.05	12)	162.25		

c Write these numbers correct to 2 decimal places

1)	3.3248	5)	0.664	9)	69.696	13)	1.7735
2)	9.878	6)	12.839	10)	0.1450	14)	0.028
3)	44.753	7)	5.9412	11)	8.332	15)	7.197
4)	0.987	8)	0.735	12)	0.074		

d

1) Multiply 4.17 by 0.6 and give your answer correct to 2 decimal places
2) Add 32.65, 9.64 and 25.14, giving your answer correct to 1 decimal place.
3) Find the value of 0.11×0.08, correct to 3 decimal places.
4) Divide 2.366 by 7, giving your answer correct to 2 decimal places.
5) Subtract 0.0044 from 0.012 and write the answer correct to 3 decimal places.
6) Find, correct to 1 decimal place, the value of $1.7 \div 4$.
7) Express the product of 0.26 and 6.36 correct to 2 decimal places.
8) Write the sum of 6.888 and 12.384 correct to 2 decimal places.
9) Find the value of $1.3 \times 1.3 \times 1.3$, correct to 1 decimal place.
10) Calculate, to 1 decimal place, the result of subtracting 2.61 from 39.

A STANDARD FORM

Standard Form (or Standard Scientific Notation) is a short way of writing very large or very small numbers.

    e.g.   Write   396000000000 in standard form

*1)   Miss off noughts **at the beginning or end** (unless the noughts at the end are significant)   396

*2)   Put a decimal point after the FIRST digit. If there is only one digit, leave it as it is.   3.96

*3)   Write $\times$ 10   3.96 $\times$ 10

*4)   Count the number of decimal places from the original number to the new one and put as a power of 10

$$\overset{\frown}{396000000000}$$

        so answer is   3.96 $\times$ 10^{11}

If the original has no whole number (if it begins with 0), the power of 10 has a minus sign

        e.g. 0.00052 $=$ 5.2×10^{-4}

REMEMBER 10 is always written 10 (not 10^1)

    e.g.   74 in standard form is 7.4×10 (not 7.4×10^1)

Some more examples

           6500000 $=$ 6.5×10^6
           502600000 $=$ 5.026×10^8
           0.000000003 $=$ 3×10^{-9}

B WRITING IN FULL

    e.g.   Write 2.7×10^5 in full

    $2.7 \times 10^5 = 2.7 \times 10 \times 10 \times 10 \times 10 \times 10$

                $=$ 270000

---

    e.g.   Write 8×10^{-7} in full

8×10^{-7} $=$ $8 \div 10 \div 10 \div 10 \div 10 \div 10 \div 10 \div 10$

                $=$ 0.0000008

Check. Your answer, written in standard form, should be the same as the question.

1 Write in standard form (The noughts at the ends are not significant)

1)	920000	6)	0.00005	11)	two hundred and nine thousand
2)	6340	7)	59000000		
3)	0.038	8)	0.426	12)	eight hundred and thirty
4)	27	9)	0.0000008	13)	forty-one million
5)	1010000	10)	910	14)	seventy-three thousand
				15)	sixty

Write in standard form (The noughts at the ends are not significant)

1)	58270	6)	8750000	11)	0.22
2)	1883	7)	0.071	12)	312000
3)	0.005891	8)	0.000018	13)	0.00000009
4)	62400000	9)	90000	14)	4250000000
5)	763287	10)	350	15)	8000

Write in full

1)	5.2×10^{4}	5)	9.77×10^{-1}	8)	1.45×10^{6}
2)	8×10^{9}	6)	3.4×10^{-6}	9)	2.8×10^{-4}
3)	1.37×10^{-2}	7)	2×10^{7}	10)	3.6×10
4)	6.1×10^{5}				

1

1) Multiply 1275 by 8000 and express your answer in standard form to 3 significant figures.
2) Add 81273, 77238, 9324 and 32806, expressing the answer in standard form
3) Divide 1.26 by 18 and give the answer in standard form
4) Subtract 0.0009 from 0.00123 and give your answer in standard form correct to 1 sig. fig.
5) Write in standard form the value of ten thousand times ten thousand
6) The population of the United Kingdom in 1980, to 2 significant figures, was 56000000. Write this number in standard form.
7) The Moon is 240000 miles (2 sig. figs.) from Earth. Express this distance in standard form.
8) The width of a hydrogen molecule is about 0.000000025 cm. What is this width in standard form?
9) The summit of Mount Everest is 8850m (3 sig. figs.) above sea level. Express this height in standard form.
10) One minute is about 0.0000019 of a year. Write this quantity in standard form.

MULTIPLICATION IN STANDARD FORM

e.g.   Multiply (7×10^4) by (4×10^2),   giving the answer in standard form.

*1)   Multiply the first numbers $\hspace{3cm} 7 \times 4 = 28$

*2)   Multiply the 'tens' by <u>ADDING</u> the powers
$$10^4 \times 10^2 = 10^6$$

*3)   Write these answers together $\hspace{2cm} 28 \times 10^6$

*4)   Change to standard form (unless it is in
standard form already) $\hspace{3cm} 2.8 \times 10^7$

e.g.   Find the value of $(8.9 \times 10^{16}) \times (9.3 \times 10^{-5})$ giving your answer in standard form to 2 sig.figs.
$$8.9 \times 9.3 = 82.77 = 83 \text{ (2 sig.figs)}$$
$$10^{16} \times 10^{-5} = 10^{11}$$
$$83 \times 10^{11} \text{ , so answer is } 8.3 \times 10^{12}$$

Some more examples of multiplying the 'tens' part

10^7	$\times$	10^8	$= 10^{15}$	$10^{-5} \times 10^3$	$=$	10^{-8}
10^3	$\times$	10^{-2}	$= 10$	$10^{-4} \times 10^{10}$	$=$	10^6
10^4	$\times$	10^{-7}	$= 10^{-3}$	$10^{-2} \times 10$	$=$	10^{-1}

 # DIVISION IN STANDARD FORM

e.g.   Divide $(4.2 \div 10^6)$ by $(6 \div 10^2)$

*1)   Divide the first numbers $\hspace{2cm} 4.2 \div 6 = 0.7$

*2)   Divide the 'tens' by
<u>SUBTRACTING</u> the powers $\hspace{1cm} 10^6 \div 10^2 = 10^4$

*3)   Write the answers together $\hspace{2cm} 0.7 \times 10^4$

*4)   Change to standard form (unless it is
in standard form already) $\hspace{2cm} 7 \times 10^3$

Some more examples of dividing the 'tens' part

$10^2 \div 10^5 = 10^{-3}$		$10^7 \div 10^{-6} = 10^{13}$
$10^{11} \div 10^{10} = 10$		$10^{-2} \div 10^{-7} = 10^5$
$10^{-2} \div 10^4 = 10^{-6}$		$10^{-3} \div 10^8 = 10^{-11}$

 If the answer works out as 10^0, miss the 'tens' out altogether (because $10^0 = 1$)   e.g. 8.4×10^0
$$= 8.4$$

a All answers should be given in STANDARD FORM

1) $(2 \times 10^5) \times (4 \times 10^7)$
2) $(5 \times 10^2) \times (3 \times 10^4)$
3) $(1.8 \times 10^3) \times (7 \times 10^2)$
4) $(9.3 \times 10^7) \times (2.4 \times 10^{-2})$
5) $(3 \times 10^{11}) \times (3 \times 10^{11})$
6) $(1.7 \times 10^{-3}) \times (4 \times 10^{-4})$
7) $(5 \times 10^4) \times (6 \times 10^3) \times (7 \times 10^2)$
8) $(6.8 \times 10^{-4}) \times (5.2 \times 10^4)$
9) $(2.5 \times 10^8) \times (2 \times 10^{-8})$
10) $(3.4 \times 10^{-7}) \times (1 \times 10^{-2}) \times (1.5 \times 10^{-1})$

b All answers should be given in STANDARD FORM

1) $(6 \times 10^8) \div (2 \times 10^3)$
2) $(9.6 \times 10^7) \div (1.2 \times 10^5)$
3) $(3.3 \times 10^{18}) \div (6 \times 10^6)$
4) $(6.3 \times 10^{-3}) \div (7 \times 10^4)$
5) $(3.74 \times 10^8) \div (1.1 \times 10^{-7})$
6) $(9.2 \times 10^{-2}) \div (8 \times 10^{-5})$
7) $(1.5 \times 10^9) \div (1.5 \times 10^{10})$
8) $(7.32 \times 10^6) \div (4 \times 10^5)$
9) $(2.73 \times 10^{-4}) \div (1.2 \times 10^5)$
10) $(5.88 \times 10^7) \div (8.4 \times 10^6)$

c All answers should be given in STANDARD FORM

1) Find the value of $(3.9 \times 10^3) \times (1.8 \times 10)$ correct to 2 sig.figs.
2) Multiply (8.23×10^{25}) by (5.2×10^{14}) giving your answer correct to 3 sig.figs.
3) Calculate the product of (8×10^4) and (3×10^5) and then divide your answer by (6×10^{12}).
4) Find the value of $\dfrac{(6 \times 10^7) \times (2.4 \times 10^4)}{(8 \times 10^8)}$
5) What is the value, correct to 1 sig. fig. of $(2.03 \times 10^5) \div (7 \times 10^{-11})$?
6) Calculate the value of $\dfrac{(7.8 \times 10^2)}{(3.75 \times 10^{-1}) \times (8 \times 10^6)}$
7) Divide (2×10^{16}) by (3×10^2), giving your answer correct to 2 sig.figs.
8) By writing the numbers in full, find the value to 3 sig. figs, of $(9.626 \times 10^7) + (8.74 \times 10^6)$
9) Write these numbers in full and then add them together (7.48×10^{-4}), (2×10^{-6}), (8.95×10^{-3}).
10) By writing the numbers in full, find the value of $(3.76 \times 10^4) - (9.73 \times 10^3)$. Write your answer to 2 sig. figs.

PLANE FIGURES

A plane figure is a figure that can be drawn on a flat surface.

TRIANGLE

A triangle is a plane figure with 3 sides

e.g.

Triangle PQR

QUAD (short for 'QUADRILATERAL')

A quad is a plane figure with 4 sides

e.g.

Quad LMJK

##

A plane figure with 5 sides is a PENTAGON
A plane figure with 6 sides is a HEXAGON
A plane figure with 7 sides is a HEPTAGON
A plane figure with 8 sides is an OCTAGON
A plane figure with 9 sides is a NONAGON
A plane figure with 10 sides is a DECAGON
All plane figures with many sides are kinds of POLYGON

##

Figures are lettered (or LABELLED) all the way round in the same direction

e.g.   This quad can be called
ABCD, BCDA, CDAB, DABC, DCBA,
CBAD, BADC or ADCB, but not
ACBD, DBCA, etc.

PARALLEL LINES

Parallel lines are groups of lines which always stay the same distance apart.   They are marked with the same kind of arrows to show that they are parallel.

e.g.

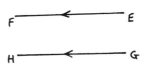

JK and LM
are parallel lines.
JK is parallel to LM.

EF and GH
are parallel lines.
EF is parallel to GH.

These four lines
are parallel.

Copy each figure and write against your copy which sort of figure it is.

e.g.  TUV is a triangle

Remember that the lettering (or labelling) goes round the figure in the correct order.

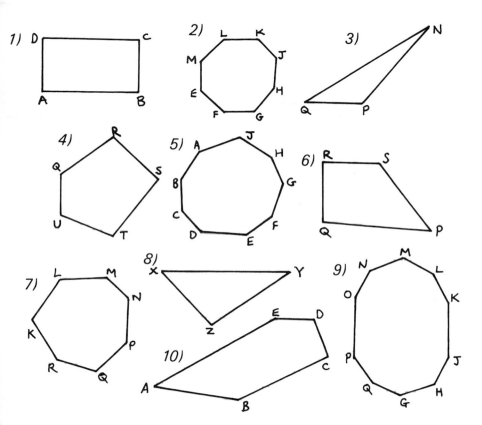

1) Draw a hexagon ABCDEF
2) Draw a quad QRST
3) Draw a triangle JKL
4) Draw a pentagon EFGHJ
5) Draw parallel lines PQ and RS. Mark the lines with arrows to show that they are parallel.

PERIMETER

The perimeter of a figure is the distance all the way round the figure.

e.g.   Find the perimeter of triangle ABC.

*Start at one corner and go right round.

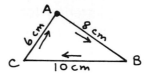

Perimeter = 8 + 10 + 6 = 24 cm

IF IN DOUBT, make a rough drawing first.

e.g.   Calculate the perimeter of a rectangular field 92 metres long and 75 metres wide.

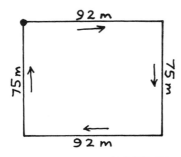

```
  92
  75
  92
+ 75
 ───
 334   = 334 metres
```

e.g.   What is the perimeter of a photograph in the shape of a rectangle 12.6 cm long and 8.7 cm wide?

```
  12.6
   8.7
  12.6
+  8.7
 ─────
  42.6            = 42.6 cm
```

e.g.   Find the perimeter of a rectangular piece of paper 3¾ cm long and 2⅓ cm wide.

$$3\tfrac{3}{4} + 2\tfrac{1}{3} + 3\tfrac{3}{4} + 2\tfrac{1}{3}$$
$$10\,\tfrac{9}{12} + \tfrac{4}{12} + \tfrac{9}{12} + \tfrac{4}{12} = 10\tfrac{26}{12}$$
$$= 12\tfrac{1}{6}\ \text{cm}$$

1

Find the perimeter of each of these figures (not drawn to scale). Remember to put the correct UNITS (e.g. m, cm, etc.) in your answer.

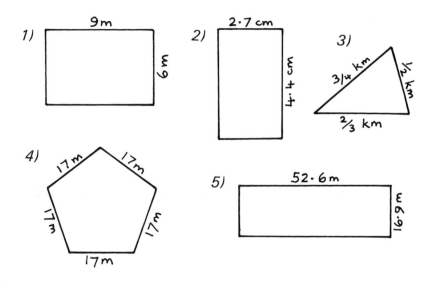

1) Find the perimeter of a rectangle 643 mm long and 455 mm wide.

2) What is the perimeter of a rectangular courtyard 19.3 m long and 15.3 m wide?

3) Calculate the perimeter of a rectangular postage stamp of length 41 mm and width 31 mm.

4) The sides of a triangle have lengths 112 mm, 112 mm and 97 mm. Calculate the perimeter of the triangle.

5) Mr Sanders wants to put a fence all round the outside of a rectangular garden 34 metres long and 18 metres wide. What length of fence will he need?

6) A spider walks all the way round the edge of a rectangular table top which measures 85 cm in length and 65 cm in width. What distance does it walk?

7) What is the perimeter of a fishpond in the shape of a hexagon with each side 6.25 m long?

8) A field in the shape of a rectangle is 250 m wide and 350 m long. A farmer walks right round the edge of the field. How far does he walk?

9) A cook wishes to place a strip of frilly paper round a square birthday cake of length (and width) 24.5 cm. What length of frilly paper will she need?

10) A wildlife reserve is in the shape of a rectangle 23 miles long and 14 miles wide. The warden drives her Land Rover round the perimeter of the reserve. How far does she drive?

A SPECIAL TYPES OF QUAD

1) TRAPEZIUM is a quad with ONE PAIR of parallel sides

e.g.

2) PARALLELOGRAM is a quad with TWO PAIRS of parallel sides

e.g.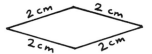

3) RHOMBUS is a quad with ALL ITS SIDES THE SAME LENGTH

e.g.

A rhombus is a special type of parallelogram.

4) RECTANGLE is a quad with FOUR RIGHT ANGLES (All its corners are square).

e.g.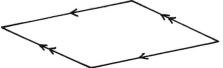

A rectangle is a special type of parallelogram. It can also be called an OBLONG if it is not completely square.

A right angle is usually marked like this

5) SQUARE is a quad with FOUR RIGHT ANGLES and ALL ITS SIDES THE SAME LENGTH

e.g.

A square is a special type of rhombus and it is also a special type of rectangle.

6) KITE is a quad with TWO PAIRS OF ADJACENT (next door) SIDES THE SAME LENGTH. It has no parallel sides.

e.g.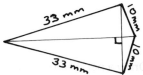

a Write down which type of quad each of these is. If it is not a 'special' type, write 'ordinary quad'.

e.g. 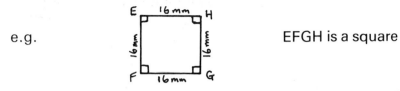 EFGH is a square

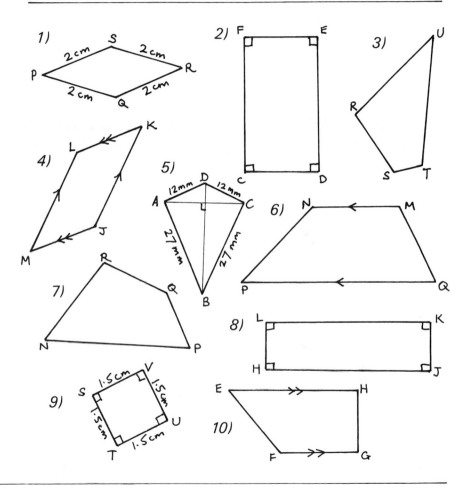

1)
2)
3)
4)
5)
6)
7)
8)
9)
10)

---

b
1) Draw a rectangle ABCD
2) Draw a kite GHJK
3) Draw a trapezium LMNP
4) Draw a square PQRS
5) Draw a parallelogram TUVW

A AREA of RECTANGLE

Area of rectangle = Length × Width

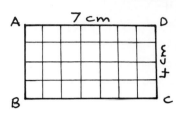

e.g. Find the area of rectangle
ABCD which is 7 centimetres
long and 4 centimetres wide

7 × 4 = 28 square centimetres

or 28 cm²

AREA is always measured in SQUARE units (e.g. square metres, square centimetres, etc.)

Square metres can be written m² (or sq.m.)
Square centimetres can be written cm² (or sq.cm.)
Square millimetres can be written mm² (or sq.mm.)

---

e.g. What is the area of the floor of a rectangular kitchen 5½ m long and 4½ m wide?

$$5½ \times 4½$$

$$\frac{11}{2} \times \frac{9}{2} = \frac{99}{4} = 24¾ \text{ m}^2$$

---

e.g. A rectangular pond has a width of 5 m and an area of 35 m². What is its length?

Area = Length × Width

Length $= \dfrac{\text{Area}}{\text{Width}}$

Length of pond $= \dfrac{35}{5} = 7$ m

B AREA of SQUARE

Area of square = (Length)² **or** Length × Length

e.g. What is the area of a
square 3.4 m long?

3.4 × 3.4

= 11.56 m²

Calculate the area of each of these rectangles (not drawn to scale)

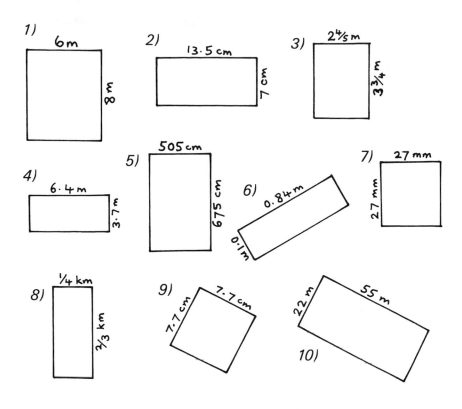

1) 6 m, 8 m

2) 13.5 cm, 7 cm

3) 2⅘ m, 3¾ m

4) 6.4 m, 3.7 m

5) 505 cm, 675 cm

6) 0.84 m, 0.1 m

7) 27 mm, 27 mm

8) ¼ km, ⅔ km

9) 7.7 cm, 7.7 cm

10) 22 m, 55 m

All the shapes in these questions are rectangles.

1) A field is 450 m long and 250 m wide. Calculate its area.
2) Calculate the area of a sticky label 43 mm long and 28 mm wide.
3) What is the area of a door of length 2.4 m, width 0.9 m?
4) A flat roof has a length of 6¾ m and a width of 3⅓ m. Find its area.
5) The cover of a magazine has an area of 630 cm² and a length of 30 cm. What is its width?
6) The length of a rug is 155 cm and its width is 90 cm. Calculate its area, and give your answer in square metres (see page 28C).
7) Write down the length of a square piece of card which has an area of 81 cm².
8) A poster is 0.6 m wide and its area is 0.51 m². How long is it?
9) The pastry top of a steak pie is in the shape of a square 180 mm long. Find its area, in square centimetres (see page 28C).
10) What is the length of a badge which has a width of 24 mm and an area of 864 mm²?

A AREA of RECTANGLE (2)

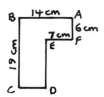

e.g. Find the area of
figure ABCDEF

*1) Write in any missing lengths

CD = AB − FE   = 14 − 7 =   7 cm

DE = BC − AF   =   19 − 6 = 13 cm

*2) Divide the figure into rectangles

*3) Work out the area of each rectangle

Area of top rectangle = 14 × 6 = 84 cm²
Area of bottom rectangle = 13 × 7 = 91 cm²

*4) Add the areas together

Area of ABCDEF is 84 + 91 = 175 cm²

e.g. Find the area of figure PQRSTUVW

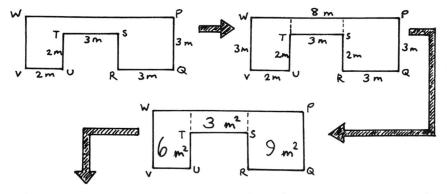

Area of PQRSTUVW is 6 + 3 + 9 = 18 m²

1 Find the area of each figure (not drawn to scale)

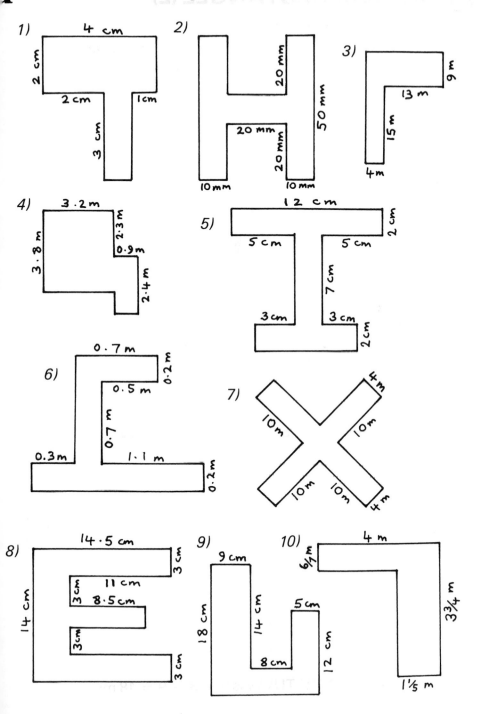

1)
4 cm
2 cm
2 cm   1 cm
3 cm

2)
20 mm
50 mm
20 mm
20 mm
10 mm   10 mm

3)
9 m
13 m
15 m
4 m

4)
3.2 m
3.8 m
2.3 m
0.9 m
2.4 m

5)
12 cm
5 cm   5 cm
2 cm
7 cm
3 cm   3 cm
2 cm

6)
0.7 m
0.2 m
0.5 m
0.7 m
0.3 m   1.1 m
0.2 m

7)
4 m
10 m   10 m
10 m   10 m
4 m

8)
14.5 cm
3 cm
14 cm
3 cm   11 cm
3 cm   8.5 cm
3 cm
3 cm

9)
9 cm
18 cm
14 cm
5 cm
8 cm
3 cm

10)
4 m
6/7 m
5 cm
12 cm
3¾ m
1⅕ m

AREA of RECTANGLE (3)

e.g.   A rectangular photograph 12 cm long and 10 cm wide is mounted on a rectangular piece of card 17 cm long and 15 cm wide.   What is the area of card not covered by the photograph?

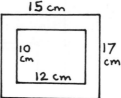

*1)   Find the area of large rectangle $17 \times 15 = 255$ cm²

*2)   Find the area of small rectangle $12 \times 10 = 120$ cm²

*3)   Subtract $255 - 120 = 135$ cm²

If in doubt, make a rough drawing.

---

e.g.   Find the area of the shaded part of the drawing (not drawn to scale)

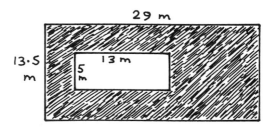

Area of large rectangle	$=$	29×13.5
	$=$	391.5 m²
Area of small rectangle	$=$	13×5
	$=$	65 m²
Area of shaded part $=$		$391.5 - 65$
	$=$	326.5 m²

All the shapes in these questions are rectangles.

1) A painting 32 cm long and 18 cm wide is placed in a frame 48 cm long and 32 cm wide. What is the area of the border round the painting (the shaded part in the drawing)?

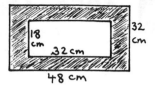

2) Ben's garden, which is 9 m long and 7.5 m wide, is all grass except for a rose bed which is 4 m long and 3 m wide. What area of grass is there in the garden?

3) Find the area of the shaded part of the drawing (not drawn to scale)

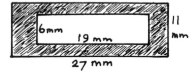

4) A carpet 6 m long, 4½ m wide is placed on a floor 8 m long, 6½ m wide. How much of the floor is not covered by carpet?

5) A flag is 30 cm long and 20 cm wide. In the middle there is a yellow rectangle 18 cm long and 10 cm wide. All the rest of the flag is green. What is the area of the green part?

6) Find the area of the shaded part of the drawing

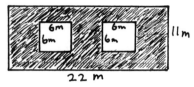

7) A rectangular courtyard consists of a pond surrounded by a concrete path. The pond is 8⅘ m long and 6¼ m wide; the courtyard is 13½ m long and 9⅓ m wide. Calculate the area of the concrete path

8) Fifteen stamps are stuck on a page of a stamp album. The page measures 24 cm by 20 cm and each stamp measures 4 cm by 2 cm. What area of the page is not covered by stamps?

9) Find the area of the **un**shaded part of the drawing

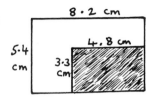

10) From a sheet of steel ⅝ m long and ¾ m wide, a hole ⅔ m long and ⅛ m wide is cut out. What area of steel remains?

AREA of TRIANGLE

Area of triangle = ½ × BASE × HEIGHT

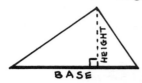
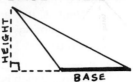

REMEMBER. The HEIGHT must always be
PERPENDICULAR (at right angles) to the base.

e.g. Find the area of triangle JKL.

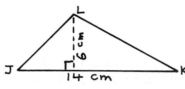

Area = ½ × 14 × 6 = 42 cm²

e.g. What is the area of a triangle with base 3½ m and
height 5 m?

Area = ½ × 3½ × 5
= ½ × ⁷⁄₂ × ⁵⁄₁ = $\frac{35}{4}$ = 8¾ m²

AREA of PARALLELOGRAM

Area of parallelogram = BASE × PERPENDICULAR HEIGHT

e.g. Calculate the area
of parallelogram ABCD

Area = 43 × 12
= 516 cm²

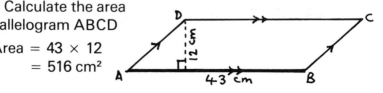

AREA of TRAPEZIUM

Area of trapezium =
½ × (BASE + TOP) × PERPENDICULAR HEIGHT

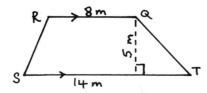

e.g. Find the area of
trapezium QRST

Area = ½ × (14 + 8) × 5
= ½ × 22 × 5
= 55 m²

Find the area of each of these triangles (not drawn to scale)

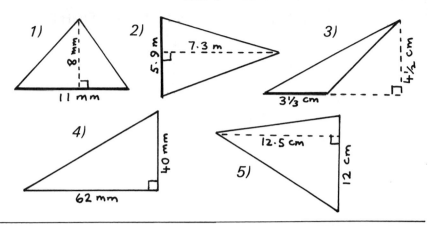

1) 8 mm, 11 mm

2) 5.9 m, 7.3 m

3) 4½ cm, 3⅓ cm

4) 40 mm, 62 mm

5) 12.5 cm, 12 cm

1) What is the area of a triangle with base 13 cm and height 7 cm?

2) Find the area of a triangle with base ½ km and height ¼ km.

3) Calculate the area of a triangle whose height is 20.5 cm and whose base length is 24 cm.

4) A triangle has a base of length 3.7 m and a perpendicular height of 6m. What is its area?

5) Find the area of a triangle which is 106 mm high and has a base 106 mm long.

Find the area of each parallelogram

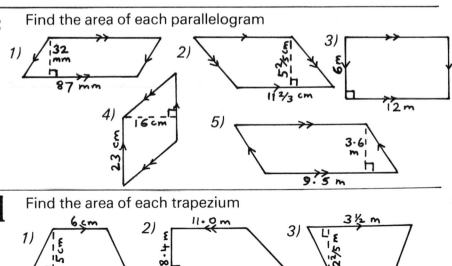

1) 32 mm, 87 mm

2) 5⅖ cm, 11⅔ cm

3) 6 m, 12 m

4) 16 cm, 23 cm

5) 3.6 m, 9.5 m

Find the area of each trapezium

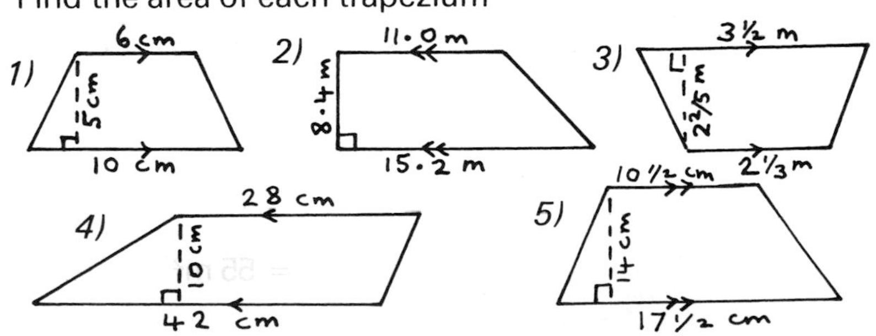

1) 6 cm, 5 cm, 10 cm

2) 11.0 m, 8.4 m, 15.2 m

3) 3½ m, 2⅖ m, 10½ cm, 2⅓ m

4) 28 cm, 10 cm, 42 cm

5) 5 cm, 4 cm, 17½ cm

SOLID FIGURES

A solid figure is a figure which takes up space. It is a three-dimensional figure.

Many solids have very complicated shapes, but two types which are fairly simple are PRISMS and PYRAMIDS.

PRISMS

A prism is a solid with both its ends (BASE and top) the same shape and size. The two ends are joined by perpendicular edges, e.g.

 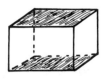

| TRIANGULAR PRISM (Its base is a triangle) | RECTANGULAR PRISM (or CUBOID) (Its base is a rectangle) | PENTAGONAL PRISM (Its base is a pentagon) | CIRCULAR PRISM (or CYLINDER) (Its base is a circle) etc. |

PYRAMIDS

A pyramid is a solid with a special shape at one end (BASE) and a corner at the other end (APEX), e.g.

| TRIANGULAR PYRAMID (Its base is a triangle) | RECTANGULAR PYRAMID (Its base is a rectangle) | SQUARE PYRAMID (Its base is a square) | CIRCULAR PYRAMID (or CONE) (Its base is a circle) etc. |

FACES, CORNERS AND EDGES

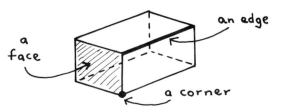

This solid has
6 FACES
8 CORNERS
12 EDGES

1 Copy each figure. Next to each drawing that you do, write 'prism' or 'pyramid' and which sort of prism or pyramid it is (e.g. pentagonal pyramid). The base has been shaded in each figure.

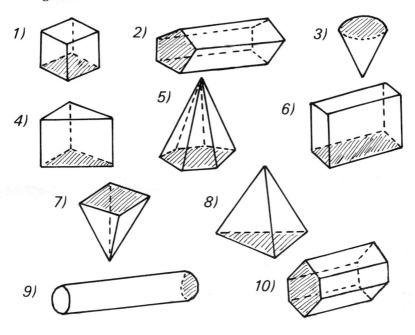

1) 2) 3)
5)
4) 6)
7) 8)
9) 10)

---

2 Write down how many FACES, CORNERS and EDGES each of these figures has.

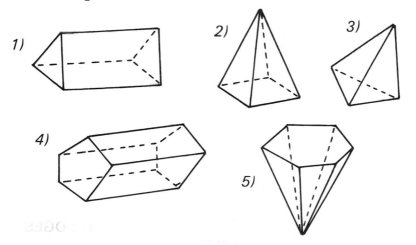

1) 2) 3)
4) 5)

NETS of SOLIDS

A net is an opened-out version of a solid, showing all its faces.

e.g.   Draw a net of a cuboid

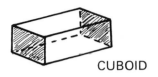

CUBOID

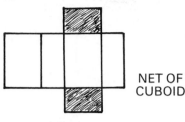

NET OF CUBOID

e.g.   Draw a net of a triangular pyramid

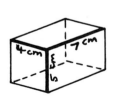

TRIANGULAR PYRAMID

NET OF TRIANGULAR PYRAMID

 SURFACE AREA of CUBOID

Total surface area of any solid figure is the SUM of the areas of all its faces.

Total surface area of a CUBOID is the sum of the areas of all six faces.

e.g.   What is the total surface area of a cuboid 7 cm long, 4 cm wide and 5 cm high?

$7 \times 4 = 28$
$7 \times 4 = 28$
$7 \times 5 = 35$
$7 \times 5 = 35$
$4 \times 5 = 20$
$4 \times 5 = \underline{20} +$
166 cm^2

Total surface area of a CUBE is 6 times the area of one face.

e.g.   Find the total surface area of a cube 9 cm long

Area of one face $=$ 9×9 $=$ 81 cm^2

Total surface area $=$ $81 \times \underline{6}$ $=$ 486 cm^2

1   Draw a net of each of these solids

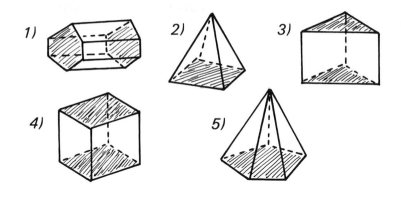

1)   2)   3)   4)   5)

---

2   Find the total surface area of each of these cuboids.

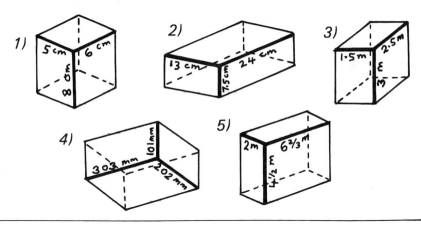

1) 5 cm   6 cm   8 cm

2) 13 cm   7.5 cm   24 cm

3) 1.5 m   2.5 m   3 m

4) 303 mm   101 mm   202 mm

5) 2 m   6⅔ m   4½ m

3

1)   Find the total surface area of a cuboid 34 cm long, 22 cm wide and 60 cm high. Give your answer in square metres (see page 28C).

2)   What is the total surface area of a cube of length 15 cm?

3)   A box in the shape of a cuboid has a length of 5.2 cm, a width of 3.8 cm and a height of 4.5 cm. Find its total surface area.

4)   Calculate the total surface area of a cubic container ⁵/₆ m long.

5)   A cuboid is 750 mm long, 600 mm wide and 400 mm high. Calculate its total surface area, giving your answer in square metres (see page 28C).

A VOLUME OF CUBOID

Volume of cuboid
= Length × Width × Height

e.g.   Find the volume of a cardboard box (cuboid)
24 centimetres long, 15 centimetres wide and 12
centimetres high.

24 × 15 × 12   =
4320 cubic centimetres
or 4320 cm³

Volume is always measured in CUBIC units, e.g. cubic metres
(m³), etc.

B VOLUME of CUBE

A cube is a prism with six square faces and with all its edges
the same length.
Volume of cube = (Length)³
or Length × Length × Length·

e.g.   What is the volume of a cube of length 8 cm?
$8^3 = 8 × 8 × 8 = 512 \text{ cm}^3$

C VOLUME of PRISM

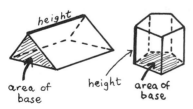

Volume of prism
= Area of base × Height.

e.g.   Find the volume of a prism if
the area of its base is 6.5 m² and its
height is 4.2 m
Volume = 6.5 × 4.2 = 27.3 m³

D LITRE

1000 cubic centimetres = 1 litre (1000 cm³ = 1l)

To express cubic centimetres in LITRES
*Divide by 1000

e.g.   Express 32856 cm³ in litres

$$\frac{32856}{1000} = 32.856 \text{ l}$$

All the objects in these questions are cuboids.

1) Find the volume of a matchbox 12 cm long, 7 cm wide and 3 cm high.
2) A water tank measures 2½ metres by 1½ metres by 1 metre. What volume of water will it hold?
3) Calculate the volume of a block of iron length 42 mm, width 24 mm and height 18 mm.
4) What is the volume of a biscuit tin 23 cm long, 20 cm wide, 9.5 cm high? Give your answer correct to 2 significant figures (see page 32B)
5) Find the volume of a pencil box 18 cm long, 7⅓ cm wide and 5½ cm high.
6) A cupboard is 50 cm long, 40 cm wide, 90 cm high. Find its volume, giving your answer in litres.
7) What is the volume, correct to 1 sig.fig., of a packing case length 43 cm, width 43 cm, height 50 cm?
8) Find the volume of a plastic container 0.7 m long, 0.4 m wide and 0.6 m high.
9) What is the volume, in litres, of an oil tank of length 80 cm, width 45 cm, height 40 cm?
10) The width of a certain box is half its length, and its height is three times its width. If its length is 32 cm, what is its volume?

---

1) What is the volume of an Oxo cube 20 mm long?
2) Find the volume of a wooden cube of length 2½ cm?
3) A cubic box is 140 cm long. What is its volume, in cubic metres (see page 28D)?
4) Calculate the volume, in litres, of a cubic room of length 3m.
5) Find, in cubic centimetres, the volume of a Rubik's cube 80 mm long

---

1) What is the volume of a prism with area of base 46 cm² and height 12 cm?
2) Calculate the volume of a prism which has a height of 5⅓ cm and a base area of 10½ cm²
3) A prismatic box is 0.75 m high and the area of its base is 0.18 m². What is its volume?
4) Find the volume of a glass prism which has a height of 40 mm and a base area of 385 mm²
5) If the area of the base of a soup tin is 34 cm² and its height is 9.5 cm, what is its volume?

SOME EXTRA QUESTIONS

1) Express 420 as a product of prime factors.

2) Estimate to 1 sig.fig. the value of $\dfrac{3.750 \times 126.65}{11.96}$

3) Find the cost of 16 fishing rods at £44.95 each.

4) What is the volume of a cube of length 1.6m?

5) Calculate the area of a rectangle 25 cm wide and 58 cm long.

6) Find the square root of $5\frac{4}{9}$

7) The numbers of tickets sold on separate days of a three-day event were 7825, 6470 and 9119. How many tickets, correct to the nearest hundred, were sold at the event altogether?

8) Find the value of 9^4

9) Express this number in (a) kilometres, (b) metres, and (c) centimetres

km			m		cm	mm
	2	6	7	5		

10) Write in short in ascending order $3 \times 11 \times 5 \times 5 \times 7 \times 3 \times 11 \times 5$

11) Write 2.4 : 5.6 : 6.4 as a ratio in its lowest terms.

12) Draw a net of this solid

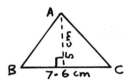

13) Write in full 8.75×10^{-7}

14) A sheet of glass with an area of 1.44 m² is cut equally into 60 small pieces. What is the area, in cm², of each small piece?

15) Find the area of triangle ABC

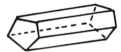

16) A chess board is divided into 64 squares. Each square is 3.5 cm long. By finding the area of each square, calculate the area of the whole chess board.

17) Find the H.C.F. of 72 and 336.

18) What special type of quad is each of these?

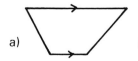

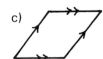

19) Calculate the perimeter of a rectangle which is 27.3 cm long and 19.9 cm wide.

20) A piece of cheese in the shape of a prism is 12.5 cm high and the area of its base is 22 cm². Find its volume.

21) The lengths of the sides of a quad are in the ratio 2 : 5 : 3 : 6. The shortest side is 10 cm long. By finding the lengths of the other sides, or by any other method you like, calculate the perimeter of the quad.

22) Find all the factors of 48.

23) Measure the length of CD in centimetres and tenths of centimetres.

24) Find the value of $(6.4 \times 10^{12}) \times (7 \times 10^{-4})$. Give your answer in standard form.

25) Express 3.67 km in m.

26) Find the area of this figure

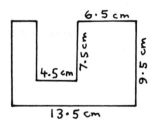

27) Find the value of 2.395 ÷ 6, correct to 2 decimal places.

28) The prices of a hard-back edition and a paper-back edition of the same book are in the ration 13 : 3. The paper-back edition costs £2.25. How much does the hard-back edition cost?

29) Write down the correct name for each of these solids

a)   b)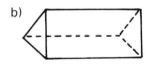

30) Find the value of $2 \times 2 \times 3 \times 3 \times 7$

31) A customer at a greengrocer's pays £10.95 for 15 kg of plums. Another customer buys 8 kg of plums, and hands £6 to the greengrocer. How much change should she receive?

32) Find the square of 2¼

33) On a square plot of land 52 m long, a rectangular bungalow 24 m long and 18 m wide is built. Calculate the area of land which is not covered by the bungalow.

34) Write 91.584 correct to 3 significant figures.

35) Find the H.C.F. of 135 and 88.

36) Express 7056 as a product of prime factors and from your answer calculate the value of $\sqrt{7056}$.

37) Multiply 3625 by 800 and give your answer in standard form.

38) Find the total surface area of a box in the shape of a cuboid 16 cm long, 11 cm wide and 4.5 cm high.

39) Find the value of $15^3 - 58^2$

40) Find the area of parallelogram EFGH

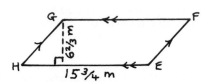

41) A collection of 444 stamps was shared between Graham, Mike and Sandy in the ratio 5 : 4 : 3. Calculate how many stamps each person received.

42) The area of a rectangular towel was 6272 cm² and its width was 56 cm. What was its length?

43) Find the L.C.M. of 90 and 66.

44) 125 cm³ of concentrated juice are used to make 2 litres of a fruit drink. How much concentrated juice would be needed to make 44 litres of the drink? Give the answer in litres.

45) Calculate the area of trapezium JKLM

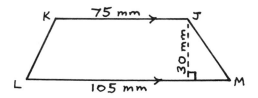

46) Find the product of 7.54 and 0.38, expressing your answer correct to 2 significant figures.

47) Measure the length of WV in millimetres.

48) By expressing 2352 as a product of prime factors, find the lowest number by which 2352 must be multiplied to make a perfect square.

49) Write down how many (a) faces, (b) corners, and (c) edges this solid has.

50) What is the volume of a suitcase in the shape of a cuboid 70 cm long, 45 cm wide and 20 cm high?